CW00864704

The Strong Tower

Stories for **tough** times

Copyright © Robert Harrison 2006
First published 2006
ISBN 1 84427 122 6

Scripture Union, 207–209 Queensway, Bletchley,
Milton Keynes, MK2 2EB, England.
Email: info@scriptureunion.org.uk
Website: www.scriptureunion.org.uk

Scripture Union Australia
Locked Bag 2, Central Coast Business Centre, NSW 2252
Website: www.scriptureunion.org.au

Scripture Union USA
PO Box 987, Valley Forge, PA 19482
Website: www.scriptureunion.org

All rights reserved. No part of this publication may be reproduced,
stored in a retrieval system, or transmitted in any form or by any
means, electronic, mechanical, photocopying, recording or otherwise,
without the prior permission of Scripture Union.

The right of Robert Harrison to be identified as author of this work
has been asserted by him in accordance with the Copyright, Designs
and Patents Act 1988.

Roger Langton has asserted his right under the Copyright, Designs
and Patents Act 1988, to be identified as illustrator of this work.

With thanks to Sue Phipps for the Guidance notes, pages 59-64.

British Library Cataloguing-in-Publication Data.
A catalogue record of this book is available from the British Library.

Printed and bound in Singapore by Tien Wah Press.

Design: kwgraphicdesign.

Scripture Union is an international Christian charity
working with churches in more than 130 countries, providing
resources to bring the good news about Jesus Christ to children,
young people and families and to encourage them to develop
spiritually through the Bible and prayer.

As well as our network of volunteers, staff and associates
who run holidays, church-based events and school Christian
groups, we produce a wide range of publications and support
those who use our resources through training programmes.

The Strong Tower

Stories for **tough** times

Robert Harrison
and
Roger Langton

with guidance notes by Sue Phipps

Contents

Introduction

for parents and carers

Troubled times. We would all like to protect our children from troubled times, but in reality we know that it is just not possible. Children *will* experience problems. Whether it's bullying, loss, family difficulties, or fears about change or what the future holds.

The world is sometimes a scary place for us adults, but we have knowledge and experience, and hopefully faith, to help us understand what is going on. Children often have incomplete information, which they process in a very subjective way. The concept of children blaming themselves when their parents separate is a familiar one, and this is just one example.

We need to be aware that different children respond to situations in different ways, and that we must not fall into the trap of looking for what is normal. A child who has experienced bereavement may not cry, but tear around the house and become disruptive at school. Very commonly, children going through troubled

times will show their distress through a change in their behaviour. Adults may perceive this as naughtiness, but tantrums, pushing the boundaries, fighting with siblings, and boisterousness can be ways to express confusion and hurt. Other children will show distress by crying, becoming withdrawn and complaining of tummy aches or feeling sick.

This section aims to show how you can use these Bible stories to help children make sense of troubled times in their lives. As adults we can find guidance in the Bible about how to live; stories about real people who met with God; and a clear message of assurance. God is constant and unchanging in a troubled world, and cares about each of us.

The Bible can help children in a similar way. Through these stories we can see that God's love does not depend on who we are, how we behave, or what sort of family we come from. These stories show that people in the

Bible got hurt, were bullied, felt lonely, confused and rejected, and also didn't behave perfectly! Yet throughout, we are shown that God is a source of strength, love and acceptance.

Using this book

We have a wonderful opportunity through this book of Bible stories to give children important messages which will help them throughout their lives. Although written thousands of years ago, the Bible has something to say to us now. God can still speak to us today.

Some of these Bible stories may have elements that relate to a child's present situation, others may remind a child of past experiences. Either way, helping a child to explore their feelings will enable them to make sense of what is happening now, or has happened in the past. We can then begin to help them deal with those feelings and more sensitively meet their needs.

Sometimes children are afraid to express feelings: fear and anxiety may be overwhelming; anger and jealousy are considered to be bad emotions. Feelings that are not acknowledged will fester, and cause bitterness, or build up like fizzy drink in a shaken bottle, ready to explode. If children can come to terms with their feelings, they can

move on, more confident in their ability to deal with problems and with a renewed sense of self-worth that comes from being loved and accepted.

So what tools do we need? Well, nothing too complicated really. First and foremost, children need our time. We are not talking about hours here; quality is more important than quantity. We need to be able to listen as well as talk. Let the child tell you what they think. Don't put words in their mouth, or worse, tell them what they should think or feel.

In helping children articulate their feelings about difficult situations, we can get a sense of what is going on in their heads, perhaps with surprising results. These stories can be used to

open up discussion about what is really going on and we can then respond appropriately. If you feel out of your depth or need more information on any of the issues which may come up, there are some addresses and websites at the end of the book.

Prayer is, of course, your most valuable tool, so before using these stories ask God to give you sensitivity and the right words to use. Pray for opportunities to explain that God is interested in us and has given us the Bible as a resource relevant to our everyday lives.

After reading the stories and talking about them, it may well be appropriate to pray with children about their situation. However, this is not a substitute for doing other necessary work. This could be correcting a child's faulty understanding of events, or giving them information. They may need you to speak to someone else on their behalf to resolve a situation.

There are some guidance notes for each

story at the end of the book, but they are not a script, they are suggestions of approaches to explore. No one can supply you with easy answers to every situation that may arise. However, a few general questions might include: Have you ever felt like … in the story? What happened? Who did you talk to about it? If the response to this last question is "no one", you can help the child think about people they know and trust who they could talk to in the future.

It would be wise to look at the questions at the end of the book *before* reading the story. If you refer to the back with the child present, they may feel that they have to do a test on the story. It is not necessary to remember every question or to ask them in a particular order. Allow the child's needs to direct your questions. If there is not a good opportunity to talk about the story during story-time, perhaps there will be a more natural opportunity over a meal, in the car, or at bedtime.

Abandoned in the desert

Genesis 21

Ishmael knew that it was his own fault. He should have kept his big mouth shut. But he didn't, and now he and his mum were abandoned in the desert.

He curled up in the shade of a desert bush and cried. He didn't care that he was crying. He had every right to cry. If he hadn't been so angry, if he hadn't let his feelings get the better of him, he would still be at home in his father's camp. But now he and his mum were all alone, in the middle of nowhere. And they were going to die.

Everything had been fine until two years ago. Ishmael had been his dad's only child, the pride of the whole family. Sarah, his stepmother, had always been cold towards him, but that didn't matter, because Ishmael was Abraham's first son. That made him special.

Then Isaac had been born: Sarah's child, her only child, her long, long-awaited child. Suddenly Ishmael wasn't important anymore. Everyone wanted to see baby Isaac, to hold him, to pet him. The dream boy had arrived and Ishmael's nightmare began.

Sarah's coolness turned to hatred. Whatever Ishmael did was wrong. If he kept out of the way, he was hiding; if he helped, he was interfering. If he played with Isaac, he was being too rough; if he left him alone, he didn't care. He did his best to avoid Sarah, but it wasn't easy. She had become a celebrity – the old woman who had had a baby.

Then came the night of the party. And what a party! They had never had a party like it for Ishmael, but this was for little Isaac. It was awful. Ishmael and his mum were the only people in the entire camp who were not invited. Ishmael was furious. He marched in, pushed over the choice calf that was being roasted over a fire, and told his startled family exactly what he thought of them: Sarah was a cruel tyrant; Isaac was a spoilt brat. He knew he was being stupid. He knew he should stop and walk away, but it was all true and it had to be said. Ishmael reminded them that Isaac wasn't the only one whom God had promised to bless; God had promised to bless him too. He was going to be the founder of a new nation as well. He, too, would have so many descendants that they couldn't be counted. An angel had said so to his mother before he was born.

He reduced Isaac's party guests to shocked silence – except for Sarah. She screamed at Ishmael's dad, telling him to do something. In one final act of defiance, Ishmael spat at baby Isaac and left.

At first light the next morning, Sarah watched smugly from the entrance of her tent as Ishmael and his mum were thrown out of the camp. His dad, Abraham, was deeply upset, and Ishmael desperately wished he could undo what he had done. Abraham gave them as much food and water as they could carry. He had hugged Ishmael with tears rolling down his wrinkled cheeks, and reminded him that he would still be the founder of a new nation, as God had promised.

Ishmael remembered that hug now, as he hid from the sun; his mouth parched, his tongue swollen. It was not going to happen. There would be no new nation. He and his mother had eaten all the food and drunk all the water. They had walked for three days without eating or drinking anything. Ishmael had made a bow and some arrows from the branches of a desert tree. He had shot at every bird that flew anywhere near them, but he missed.

"There must be water here somewhere," his mother had insisted. "Otherwise the birds wouldn't be here."

The two of them had chased after every mirage caused by the burning sun on the hot desert floor. Each time, the promised water had vanished as they approached.

Now he had no energy left. There were plenty of mirages but he had run out of hope. Ishmael wanted to be strong, but he had failed. He was the one who crumpled first. His mum had dragged him over the stony ground to the baking shade of the nearest bush.

He licked the salty tears from his cheeks and hands. He could see his mum, Hagar, sitting straight and proud, staring out across the taunting desert, scattered with pools of shimmering, reflected light. What if one of them really *was* water? It was too late.

Ishmael watched as his mother's head wilted, her shoulders began to shudder – she was crying too.

He longed for his dad. His dad, though old, was strong. His dad would have rescued them. But his dad had chosen Isaac above Ishmael, and Sarah above Hagar. Another large tear crawled down Ishmael's dusty face.

Hagar suddenly sat bolt upright. *What was it?* Ishmael propped himself up on his elbows. She was listening to something. *Could it be the angel?* The last time the angel spoke to her, before he was born, she had run away from Abraham because of Sarah. *Could it be the angel again?* It was a wild hope.

Hagar stood up. She turned and walked towards Ishmael. There was a light in her eyes and a brightness in her face. Ishmael couldn't help hoping. She bent down and stretched out a hand.

"Come on Ish, my love, you can do it." She pulled him to his feet. "My angel has come back," she explained. "God heard you crying. Everything's going to be all right."

She dragged him out of the shade and the sun, towards the biggest of the desert mirages. Ishmael was too weak to say anything. He hoped his mother was right. He feared that the mirage's promised water would change into stony desert at any moment.

His mum was still speaking about the angel. They were getting closer. The mirage was still there.

Splash!

Real water!

Splash – God had heard him crying!

Splash – God still loved him!

Splash, splash – God kept his promise!

Ishmael and Hagar fell on their faces in the pool; sucking, slurping, bathing cracked lips and swollen tongues. Ishmael *was* going to found a new nation. It was true.

Jealous brothers

Genesis 37

"One day my brothers will bow down to me," Joseph told himself as he walked through the fields to meet them.

Joseph's dad had sent him to check up on his older brothers and their sheep. Joseph knew what would happen when he found them. They would tease him, bully him, push him and slap him. They always did. They hated him. But Joseph had a dream. He had dreamt it twice: in one dream some stars bowed down to him – one star for each brother; another time it was the bundles of corn that his brothers had just harvested. Somehow, Joseph knew that these dreams came from God.

He had ten brothers, all older than him. They were half-brothers, the children of his dad's other wives. But Joseph's dad loved *his* mum more than the others; everyone knew that. His dad told everyone how special Joseph was, and had even given him an expensive embroidered coat. That's why his brothers hated him. They were jealous.

Joseph climbed to the top of another hill. His magnificent coat billowed in the wind. Its gold and silver threads sparkling in the sunlight reminded him of the stars in his dream. His brothers were below him in the valley, with their sheep. Joseph watched them for a while, imagining all ten of them on their knees in front of him.

When the brothers saw Joseph, they huddled together. They were talking about him. He was suddenly afraid. Simeon was doing the talking, and he was the worst of the lot. They were planning something bad; he could feel it.

Reuben, the oldest, walked away from the group. He disagreed with them. Reuben was the sensible one. The other brothers stopped talking and walked up towards Joseph.

Joseph's heart was thumping. There were none of the usual insults. The brothers were silent. They wanted to hurt him. He could see it in their faces. He turned and ran – up the hill.

The brothers chased him. They were older, stronger, and faster. As he scrambled up the rocky hillside, Joseph remembered his dream. One day these hateful brothers would bow to him.

What a stupid time to think that! he told himself. He concentrated on running. They were close now. Strong hands grabbed him.

"Reuben!" Joseph shouted.

His eldest brother was sulking in the valley.

Joseph tried a scream. "REUBEN!"

Reuben climbed towards them. "I told you not to hurt the boy," he called.

"We're not going to hurt him," Simeon mocked. "We're going to kill him. And I'm having that coat."

Simeon tugged at Joseph's collar. There were so many hands gripping his arms and legs that he couldn't move. Reuben was shouting for them to stop.

The brothers wrestled the precious coat off Joseph, letting out a wild cheer when it was finally free. Simeon stood up, pulled it round his own shoulders, and danced a stupid dance. Reuben walked away.

Joseph's dream still nagged at his mind. They'll bow down to you Joseph, it seemed to say.

"No they won't," he replied in his thoughts. "They're about to kill me."

Simeon stopped dancing, and said coldly, "Let's do it."

Joseph's heart sank. Strong arms lifted him off the ground and carried him off. He wriggled and kicked and twisted. "Don't kill me," he pleaded. "Please don't kill me."

"Shut up!" Simeon snapped.

"Hit me," Joseph begged, desperate to distract them from anything worse. "Hit me as hard as you can."

"We will if you don't shut up," Simeon warned.

That was what Joseph hoped for. Wild with panic he shouted, "Come on then, weaklings. Hit me. Hurt me."

"Here it is," Simeon announced.

Whatever Joseph's brothers had planned was about to happen. He was about to die. He screamed. This was the end. He was falling, falling into darkness. His brothers cheered. He remembered his dream. Then... Thud.

Joseph was alone, it was totally dark. His back hurt, his head ached. He was surrounded by silence.

"Hello?" he called out. His voice echoed around him. "Help!" he shouted louder. He crawled around and worked out that he was in an empty water storage cistern. He tried to climb the walls but they were too smooth. He felt for a puddle of water that he could drink. There wasn't one.

He cried. There was nothing else to do. He couldn't climb out. No one could hear him. He was going to die.

A vivid image flared up in his mind. The sun and moon and eleven stars were bowing down to him. It was his dream. Joseph was angry. His dream was useless; it had caused all this trouble. He ignored it, and thought about his mum: she was expecting a baby. Maybe it would be a brother, a real brother. His dream fought back. He felt strangely calm. The dream swept away his fear. He knew it was from God. He would get out of this cistern. His brothers would bow down to him.

The lid to the cistern scraped open. Light poured in. A face appeared. "It's your lucky day, dream boy." Simeon's voice was cruel. He threw down a rope and told Joseph to tie it round himself. Other faces appeared, strange faces.

"What's happening?" he shouted anxiously.

Simeon laughed. "We've done a deal with some Ishmaelites," he replied.

Ishmaelites! The Ishmaelites were their enemies; there was an ancient feud between the tribes. Joseph's dream flooded back into his mind. "Trust me," it told him.

The rope tightened, and lifted Joseph off the floor.

"Trust me," the voice in his mind said as he swung helplessly in the darkness.

Hands heaved Joseph out into the light, but the rope kept pulling. It was dragging him along the ground. Sharp stones were ripping and tearing his skin. A stick crashed across his back. "Get up, you fool," a voice shouted. Joseph struggled to his feet. The rope was attached to a camel, and the camel was following a long line of other camels. Where were they taking him?

He looked back at his brothers. Simeon waved a large purse of money and shouted, "Goodbye, Joseph. Sweet dreams!"

They had sold him. He was being taken to Egypt, as a slave.

■ ■ ■

In the years that followed, Joseph rose from household slave to become Prime Minister of all Egypt. At that time, a terrible famine forced his brothers to travel to Egypt to buy food. They bowed down before the Prime Minister, begging for help. They didn't know until later that he was their long-lost brother.

The brave sister

Exodus 2

Miriam held her breath and didn't move. There were people coming – Egyptians. She couldn't risk being found.

Their voices were so close that she could have reached out through the tall reeds and touched their expensive clothes. She caught quick glimpses of them through the rushes. It was someone very important. Who is it? she wondered.

Miriam knew that the slightest sound would give her away. Struggling to hold her breath and stay still, she waited…

The sounds faded. Softly and carefully, she let out a long breath. Her heart was leaping against her ribs. She leaned forward and peered towards the river. The little reed basket was still where she had put it, bobbing on the water. Everything was all right.

Then Miriam's curiosity got the better of her. She wanted to know who had just passed. It was someone very rich and very important. She leaned forwards and looked along the riverbank. She saw servants and slaves in lilac linen dresses; she saw attendants in brightly coloured capes, and in the middle of them – she could hardly believe it – stood the daughter of the king of Egypt!

Balanced among the reeds, Miriam watched as attendants removed the princess' gold chains, and unclipped her magnificent shoulder cape. Two slaves stooped down to remove the princess' sandals. A servant carefully unwrapped her fine cotton dress. The king's daughter then slipped effortlessly into the cool water of the river.

Miriam knew she had just witnessed something that she should never have seen, but she was enchanted by the beauty of the princess and all the people around her. The enchantment was broken by a tiny sigh. It came from the basket on the river. It was Miriam's baby brother. The awfulness of the situation crashed over her like a cold wave.

She was a Hebrew slave. All her family were slaves. The Hebrews weren't pampered like the palace slaves she had just been watching. They were labourers. And the king had decided that there were too many of them, so he had ordered that all baby Hebrew boys be killed at birth. That was why Miriam's little brother was in a basket among the reeds. Their mum had hidden him from the Egyptians for three months, but it was too risky to keep him any longer.

Miriam's dad had painted the basket with tar to make it float; her mum had wrapped the baby up in clean linen, and Miriam had carried the precious package to the river. They hoped that some Egyptian peasants would find the child and care for him. Now the whole plan had been ruined by the arrival of the king's daughter.

Miriam watched, and listened. There were footsteps approaching along the riverbank. It was the princess' attendants. They were very close to the basket. It was quite well hidden; she had placed it where someone might find it if they were gathering reeds to sell. Princesses certainly didn't gather reeds, but she was now swimming among them, ever closer to the tight clump of bulrushes where Miriam had put her brother.

Miriam was holding her breath again. She started to pray. Her mum had taught her to pray

to the God who made the world and the stars.

"Please God," Miriam prayed. "Don't let her see him." She added, "God, you made the river, you made the reeds. Make him safe."

A moment later, the very thing that Miriam most feared, happened. The princess stretched out a slender arm and pointed at the tar-covered basket. Miriam's mouth hung open in silent horror. The princess ordered an attendant to fetch the basket and swam to the shore. The basket was handed to her.

Miriam didn't want to watch. The princess studied the unusual parcel. She then placed her ringed fingers under the papyrus lid and lifted it.

"Waaaaaaaaaaaah!"

The baby cried, and the princess smiled coyly, cradling the basket in her wet arms. She stepped out of the river, and attendants gathered around her, with her clothes. When dressed, the princess knelt down, placed the basket on her lap and investigated its contents more closely. She was now so close to Miriam that the Hebrew girl could see everything through the slatted curtain of reeds.

The princess unwrapped the linen that covered the baby and let out an excited squeal.

"It's one of the Hebrew babies," she declared. Everyone gathered in for a closer look. The basket was discarded and the princess

clutched Miriam's brother to her chest. "He's hungry," she cooed.

Miriam suddenly had an idea. Without a second thought, she stood up and stepped forwards. In a moment she was standing in front of the king's daughter. It was the bravest, craziest, cleverest, most wonderful thing she had ever done.

The kneeling princess looked calmly up at the slave girl, dressed in the distinctive cloth of the Hebrews.

Miriam knew that she had to speak first.

"Please, Your Highness," she said with an inexperienced bow, "shall I find a Hebrew woman to feed the baby for you?"

Miriam looked directly into the elegantly made-up eyes of the royal daughter. The baby had stopped crying, but Miriam didn't look down. She held the princess' gaze.

Everyone was waiting for the princess' reply. Inside the palace, any slave who dared to approach a princess uninvited would be killed immediately. But Miriam didn't feel afraid. She felt as though her whole body was filled with deep calm. It wasn't her own calm. It was something stronger and deeper.

The princess smiled – a rich and wonderful smile.

"Yes, do that." Her voice rang like a pure bell in Miriam's ears. Everyone relaxed. Miriam darted a quick glance at her baby brother. He was watching her.

The princess looked at him too. "Yes," she repeated. "Find me a Hebrew woman to nurse him for me. I will pay her. Then, when he no longer needs milk, he will live at the palace as my son." She hugged him close to her face. "I shall call him Moses." The princess looked up at Miriam. "Run along then!"

Miriam turned and ran through the reeds. She skipped across the lush riverside meadow. She laughed up the dusty track, and smiled her way through the bustling streets of the royal city. She knew exactly which Hebrew woman she would ask to nurse the princess' baby – Moses' own mother!

A night of panic

Exodus 14,15

Gershom's ears were ringing. Everyone around him was screaming and shouting: "The Egyptians are coming!"

Hundreds of angry people crowded round Gershom and his dad.

"Moses," they shouted, "the Egyptians are coming after us, and we're going to die! It's all your fault! You should have left us in Egypt."

Gershom was frightened too. But it wasn't the Egyptians who scared him; it was his own people, the Israelites. They were all blaming his dad, shouting:

"Why did you bring us here?"

"At least the Egyptians fed us and protected our homes. Now they're going to kill us."

Gershom ran to his tent and cried.

The Egyptians were getting closer. Everyone was terrified. The people pushed and shoved closer to Moses. They were shouting:

"Do something, you idiot!"

"If they catch us, we will all be taken back to Egypt!"

"We will be slaves again!"

"They'll kill us!"

Gershom hadn't been born in Egypt. He hated Egypt. The Egyptians were cruel. They had forced his mum to work as a slave. They had threatened to kill his dad. Gershom himself had been lashed by their whips several times. But his dad, Moses, had changed all that. Moses had shown the Egyptian king whose god was the real God! And the king had let them go, all of them, thousands of them. No more slave labour, no more whips, no more insults.

On the night that they had walked away from Egypt, everyone had been glad to leave. Moses had been their hero.

When Moses had led the Israelites away from slavery, Gershom had been at the very front, holding his dad's hand. His friends had run up to join him, and they'd all raced ahead. They wanted to be the first to escape.

"Head for the fire in the sky," Moses had shouted after them. "Follow God's fire." There was a huge column of bright light hanging between the clouds and the ground. They had never seen anything like it before.

But Moses had seen God's fire before, when he was a shepherd in the mountains. God had spoken to him from the flames, and told him to go to Egypt to rescue the Israelites and bring them home to the mountains.

Ever since the Israelites had left Egypt, God had given them a column of thick cloud to follow during the day, and God's fire had led the way at night.

Every night Gershom and his friends tried to catch up with it, but they never succeeded.

It was a long journey. At first they walked during the day and the night, because they were afraid that the Egyptians might chase after them. There was no proper food to eat, and they slept in tents. They never stopped for long. Gershom didn't like it.

"Can't we stay here, Dad?" he would ask. "When can we have a decent meal?"

But they always set off again. In the second week, they walked only during the day. God's thick cloud still went ahead of them, but the children had given up chasing it. Gershom's legs ached. His feet hurt.

"Are we nearly there?" he kept asking.

When they came to the shore of the sea, Gershom asked, "Are we there now?"

"No," Moses replied. "We're going to the mountains to meet God." So the people set up camp by the sea.

And then it happened, the thing that everyone was afraid of more than anything else. First they noticed a cloud of dust in the distance. Then they saw the sun glinting off the chariots. The king was coming after them! They were going to be captured, or killed. That was why everyone was shouting at Moses. They didn't know what to else to do.

When Moses had first arrived in Egypt, the Israelites had thanked God. But the king had been angry with Moses, and had made the Israelites work even harder. Then everyone had turned against Gershom's dad. Those had been horrible times; even Gershom's friends had refused to play with him. Now it was happening all over again.

The Israelites were now caught between the sea and the Egyptians. The people knew that Moses was the only one who could help them. Gershom ran out of his tent.

"Do something, Dad!" he yelled. "We can't go back!" His voice was lost in the crowd.

His dad turned and looked at him.

"Gershom," he said urgently, "get my staff."

Moses' staff was an old branch of wood that he had used when he was a shepherd in Midian. In Egypt, God had used the staff to turn water into blood, and dust into gnats. Once, God had even turned the staff into a snake. It was these amazing things that had persuaded the king to let the Israelite slaves go. Gershom raced back to the tent and grabbed the staff. He was suddenly excited. Perhaps God would do something wonderful again.

When he returned to his dad, the people were still angry and scared. The Egyptians were getting nearer. Everyone was screaming in terror.

Moses called out, "Come with me."

The whole crowd followed him to the water's edge. Gershom was carrying the staff. Moses walked into the water, taking his staff from Gershom, and held his arm above the water. He prayed to God.

Suddenly a wind blew up. It was strong and cold, and it started to move the water. Everyone watched in amazement. The sea was being pushed apart! Water that had been up to Moses' knees was now down by his ankles. Gershom was so excited that he jumped up and down on the beach.

"Hooray!" he shouted.

Moses turned round to the people. "Go back to your tents and sleep," he told them. "God has heard your crying. In the morning, you will walk through the middle of the sea."

Gershom went back to his tent, but he couldn't sleep properly. All through the night he could hear the powerful wind pushing the water apart. He could also hear the distant clatter of angry Egyptian soldiers. They had been stopped in their tracks because a thick fog had come down around them. Everyone was waiting for morning.

"Gershom! Gershom!" a voice was calling. He woke up. He had been asleep under the stars; the tent had disappeared. "Wake up, Gershom," his dad was saying. "It's time to go."

Gershom jumped up. Had it all been a dream? He looked towards the Egyptian army; the fog was still there. He looked at the sea. There was a wide road straight through the middle of it, and a high wall of water on either side.

"We're going to the mountains!" Moses shouted. The message echoed through the camp. Everyone was excited. Butterflies fluttered in Gershom's stomach.

"Can I carry your staff, Dad?" he asked.

"Not today," Moses said. "We're going down God's road, straight through the sea."

Gershom and his friends charged ahead. The boys and girls ran down to where the water used to be, but now their feet thudded on dry ground. Everyone was laughing. Gershom's dad was their hero again. Some people started singing.

"God has rescued us," they sang. "No more slavery. No more beatings."

They were free at last. The Egyptians wouldn't catch them now. They were following God's cloud and fire. They were going to the mountains. They were going to meet God.

A voice in the night

1 Samuel 1,2

Eli's sons were having yet another party. Samuel could hear the noise of men laughing and women shrieking outside the tent.

He snuggled up under his thick woollen cloak and tried to sleep, but he couldn't. On the other side of the heavy curtain that divided the Tent of God in two, he could just hear the gentle snoring of his foster-father, the old priest Eli. Samuel and Eli were the only people who slept in the Tent of God, and now that Eli was asleep, Samuel was all alone.

Eli's sons were the chief priests – they had inherited the position from their father – but they had no respect for God. Every day they stole food from people's sacrifices and used it for their parties. Eli knew what was going on, but he said nothing. He was afraid of both his sons. So was Samuel.

Samuel pulled the tickly woollen cloak over his face and breathed deeply. It smelled of his mother. Tears welled up behind his eyes. It was months since he had last seen his mum; and it

would be many more before he would see her again. She came every autumn, and she always brought him a new cloak. Her yearly visit was the highlight of Samuel's life. She had handed him into Eli's care when he was just three years old, to keep a promise that she had made to God before he was born. Samuel had become a child priest. Every day he helped his foster-father to look after the Tent of God, and did his best to avoid Eli's sons.

The lonely silence inside the tent was suddenly interrupted. Eli was calling him.

"I'm coming," Samuel replied. He jumped up and undid the gold clasps that separated the Most Holy Place from the entrance area. Through the curtain, the air was rich with the smell of olive oil from the seven lamps that flickered on their golden stand. Samuel nudged the old man.

"What do you want?" he asked.

Eli turned over on his mat. "I want to sleep," he grunted.

Samuel was confused. He went back to the far end of the tent, fastened the clasps on the curtain, and curled up under his cloak. Outside, Eli's sons were loudly mocking the people who had come to worship that day.

Samuel's mum had come to worship at the Tent of God, years earlier, and had begged God for a son. She had promised that if he answered her prayer, she would give the child to serve God. Samuel was that son.

Eli called again. "Samuel, Samuel!"

Samuel stood up, opened the curtain, walked past the lamps, and shook his foster-father awake. This time Eli was cross.

"I didn't call you," he growled. "Go back to sleep."

While Samuel carefully closed the ancient curtain a second time, the night was flooded with angry swearing from Eli's elder son. Samuel hid under his cloak, pushing a finger tightly into each ear.

"Samuel, Samuel," the voice called again. He wasn't imagining it. It was loud and clear, and not at all muffled by his thick cloak or his pressing fingers.

He went back to Eli. "You did call me," he insisted.

Eli sat up and looked at the boy through clouded eyes. He took Samuel's hand and pulled him to sit beside him. This time the old priest's voice was gentle.

"It's not me, Samuel," he said. "It is God who's calling you. Go back to bed, and if he calls you again, say: 'Speak, Lord, your servant is listening.'"

Samuel's stomach felt tight as he lay back down. He had never heard of God actually talking to someone, even a priest. He lay still, staring up at the rectangular shape of Israel's greatest treasure, the Ark of the Covenant. In the darkness, he could just make out the shape of the two gold angels on its lid.

The voice came again, just as before. The sound did not come from behind the curtain; it came from between the golden angels. Samuel sat up instantly, panicking to remember Eli's instructions.

"Speak," he said uncertainly, "I'm – er – your servant is listening."

■ ■ ■

Samuel woke up to the sound of Eli coughing. It was light outside. For a few moments he lay still, looking up at the deep red roof of the Tent, and remembering what the voice of God had told him during the night. He didn't know whether he should tell Eli. It was bad news.

He stood up, folded his mother's cloak, and laid it in the corner. Then he slipped on his leather sandals, wondering how Eli would react if he told him what God had said.

God was about to punish Eli's sons for all the horrible things they had done. He was also going to punish Eli for not trying to stop them. Samuel was pleased about the sons, but he loved Eli. Eli had been his father and his grandfather, his teacher and his master, for as long as he could remember. He was a caring, gentle man.

Samuel picked up his purple and gold robe, and went to open the entrance to God's Tent. He walked straight past Eli.

"Samuel!" his foster-father called from beside the tall lamp stand.

"Yes?" Samuel replied cautiously.

"Tell me what the Lord said to you, my son," Eli said. "Don't hide it from me."

Samuel looked at the blind old man whose fumbling hands were trimming the lamp wicks. The news would break his heart. He took Eli's bony hand, guided him to a low bench, and told him everything. God had had enough of Eli's greedy sons. He was about to do something that would make people's ears tingle when they heard about it.

Eli listened in silence, while Samuel broke the bad news as gently as he could. When he had finished, the old man said nothing. He only gripped more tightly onto the boy's hand. Eli's elder son poked his head inside the tent. His hair was a mess. He looked down at Samuel, belched loudly, and disappeared.

Eli spoke. His voice was steady but thick with sadness.

"God is our King, Samuel," he said. "He will do what is right."

You're only a child
1 Samuel 17

David couldn't understand it. Why were all the adults so scared? Goliath was only a man!

David wasn't a soldier; he was only a boy, and a shepherd. He was visiting the Israelite battle-camp to deliver some food to his elder brothers. He had arrived just as the Philistine and Israelite armies were taking their positions for battle. They had been doing this every day for weeks, but the battle itself had still not begun.

The Israelite soldiers, who a moment earlier had been laughing and joking, suddenly went quiet. Alarm spread through the camp.

"Goliath's coming," people gasped.

David put down the food for his brothers, and ran to the front. A tall, broad, bearded Philistine soldier was standing between the armies. He was covered from head to toe with thick bronze armour. With Goliath was a shield-bearer, a full-grown man who looked like a child beside the enormous Philistine.

"Are you going to fight or not?" the big man roared at the Israelites. There was silence

around David; all the Israelite soldiers were staring up at Goliath like frightened rabbits. "Send someone to fight me, man to man," the Philistine challenged. "If he kills me, you all win. If I kill him," here he allowed a sickening pause, "you all lose."

David looked up and down the Israelite line expectantly. No one moved.

He heard two soldiers whispering. "What's the reward for the man who kills this Philistine?" one asked.

"A sack of gold, at least," the other replied.

"He gets to marry the princess," a third added.

David was amazed. With such a huge prize on offer, he couldn't understand why there wasn't a queue of soldiers lining up to face the overgrown Philistine.

Goliath continued to taunt the Israelite soldiers. "Come on you cowards," he shouted.

"Fight me!"

"Who does this man think he his?" David asked out loud. "Does he think he'll get away with insulting the army of God?"

The eyes of the Israelite soldiers turned to him in amazement.

"What did you say the reward is, for killing this godless thug?" David asked.

"Huge wealth, and marriage to the king's daughter," someone said.

Before David could say another word, he felt a heavy slap across the back of his head.

"Ow!" he yelled, turning to see the angry face of his oldest brother.

"What are you doing here, squirt?" his brother growled in a hoarse whisper. "Why aren't you in the desert looking after your silly sheep?"

David sneaked away, rubbing his head, and spoke to a different group of soldiers. He worked his way along the Israelite line, always asking the same question: "What reward will King Saul give to the man who kills Goliath?"

News about David's interest spread, and suddenly, one of the Israelite generals marched up to him and escorted him to meet the king.

David looked into King Saul's eyes. The king was even more afraid than his soldiers.

"You don't have to worry about Goliath," David announced. "I'll fight him for you."

"Don't be so stupid," the king snorted. "You're only a boy. This Philistine is a trained soldier."

David was disappointed by the king's reaction. "I'm a shepherd," he explained. "Lions and bears often attack my sheep to snatch an easy meal." He held up the small leather sling that was tucked into his belt. "I've killed loads of them with this. That Philistine – with all his insults against God – will be easy."

King Saul slumped into his throne with relief.

At last there was someone to take away Israel's embarrassment, even if he was only a boy. "Go on then," he said. "And God be with you."

The king lent David his own helmet, sword and armour, but they were far too big and heavy. David could hardly walk in them. So he took off the expensive armour and hooked his leather sling back into his belt.

"God protected me from the lions and the bears," he told them. "He'll protect me from this Philistine just the same."

The king and the generals marched him up to the battle line. On the way, David stopped at a small stream and carefully chose five smooth, round stones. He slipped them into his pocket. When they reached the Israelite army, the king and the generals stayed in the line, leaving David to step out alone towards the mighty Philistine champion.

Goliath roared with laughter. "Do you think I'm a dog," he mocked, "coming to fight me with a stick?"

David stood still and looked up at the man he was about to fight. So much slower than a lion, he thought. And, even with all that metal armour, less protected than any bear. He quickly spotted where Goliath's armour left him unprotected. At this range, with the help of God, David concluded, I can't miss.

The Philistine and Israelite armies silently gathered around David and Goliath. The Philistines began cursing and jeering. The Israelites were sick with worry. If David lost – and they couldn't see how he might win – they would all be slaughtered.

"Come on then," Goliath bellowed.

There was silence.

"You are coming against me with a sword, and a javelin." David's voice was high and squeaky compared with Goliath's. "But I come against you in the name of God."

Goliath grabbed his spear and began to run. He charged at David with long, thundering strides. David scampered to meet him, snatching a stone from his pocket and sliding it into his sling; it was something he had done a thousand times. Both armies held their breath. As soon as David was in range, he raised the sling and swung it around his head. He took aim and flung the stone towards Goliath's face. It struck the great man right in the middle of his forehead. The Philistine champion faltered, tripped and slumped to the ground.

A thousand soldiers, several generals and two kings watched, amazed, expecting Goliath to haul himself upright for a second charge.

David calmly tucked the sling into his belt and tossed aside the four remaining stones. Goliath never moved again.

The miraculous oil jar

2 Kings 4

It was their last chance, their final hope. Tomorrow, both boys would be sold as slaves.

Everything had gone wrong for Elijah since the day his dad had fallen ill. Now, when he thought things could not get worse, when God seemed a million miles away, his mum had told him about the moneylender, and about being sold.

Elijah was the oldest of two brothers. His dad had named him after Israel's greatest prophet. The name meant "The Lord is God." His dad had believed that. He had been a village prophet; people had paid him to tell them stories about God, and to pray on their behalf. Being a prophet's son was great. Everyone liked you. Sometimes when Elijah Junior (as his dad called him) had walked through the village, someone would run out and give him a large loaf of freshly baked bread – just like that.

But then his dad had fallen ill.

"God will do a miracle," everyone said. "He'll cure your dad, you'll see."

But he didn't. Dad had grown more and more ill. Soon the people weren't so sure. "He must have done something wrong," they said among themselves. They had never said this in front of Elijah, but he had noticed the change. There had been no more gifts of fresh bread, only an embarrassed silence wherever he went.

Then Dad had died. The matter had been quickly decided in the minds of the villagers. It was God's punishment. The prophet *had* sinned, and he should have known better. The embarrassed silences had been replaced by insults and slammed doors. If God had turned against the prophet's family, the villagers believed that they should too.

Now, nobody brought them food. Elijah's mum had borrowed money, planning to find work to pay it back. But no one would hire her. She had sold their donkey. Then they had had food for a while. She had borrowed more money, and travelled to other villages in search of work. It had been no better. The rumour had spread: the prophet's family is cursed by God.

Elijah hadn't known what to think. Were they right?

His mum had sold the furniture and their best clothes, but it hadn't been enough to repay the moneylender. At night, Elijah would scour the deserted market for scraps of food. Once he had found a gold coin in the dust. For a short while it had made him believe in his dad's God again. But now the money was spent, his faith was spent too.

The moneylender was due back tomorrow. If Elijah's mum didn't pay the debt, he and his brother, Aaron, would be taken to the market and sold as slaves. They had nothing: nothing in their purses, nothing on their shelves, nothing in their bellies.

There was just one hope. The great prophet Elisha was visiting the village. He had known Elijah Junior's dad. Perhaps he could help.

Elijah's mum made the boys wash. She washed their only remaining clothes and hung them up to dry. Then the three of them huddled together and prayed to God as hard as they could. When the clothes were dry,

mum marched the boys to Elisha, who was sitting under a tree telling a story about God rescuing his people from slavery in Egypt. Elijah was angry. Where was this God when he had prayed for his dad to recover? It wasn't fair.

When he had finished, Elisha looked up. He recognised Elijah's mum and gave his sympathy at the death of her husband.

"How can I help?" he asked.

None of them knew what to say.

"Tell me," he said, "what do you have left in your house?"

"All we have," Mum said, "is a small amount of oil in a jar. But we have nothing to cook with it."

"That is enough," the prophet assured her. "Ask your neighbours to give you empty jars. Don't just ask for a few, gather as many as you can. Take them to your house, shut the door, and pour the oil out of your own jar."

Elijah's mum clasped her hands over her mouth in wonder. Aaron ran off towards the village, shouting, "What are you waiting for?"

But Elijah thought it was a stupid idea. What was the point?

Then he looked into the prophet's eyes. Elisha wasn't mocking. He cared. His eyes implored Elijah Junior to trust God, as his dad had done. Elijah turned and ran, quickly overtaking his mum and brother.

He knocked at the door of the first house he came to.

"The prophet has told us to collect empty jars," he announced.

The mention of Elisha did the trick. The door was slammed in Elijah's face, but just before slamming it, the woman said, "Wait there."

He waited. When the door opened a second time, the woman thrust an armful of jars in his direction, then slammed it again. He ran home and gave them to his mum, who started washing them and sent him to fetch more. At the next house, there were so many jars that Elijah borrowed a small hand cart. He kept the cart for the rest of the afternoon. The two brothers pulled it together. Elijah knocked on doors, while Aaron filled the cart. Word of the prophet's instruction spread and the boys sometimes found piles of empty jars waiting for them.

By sunset, they had been to every house in the village, and had hundreds of pots and jars. As the light faded, Elijah's mum picked up her own small jar, which contained a little oil. She began to pour the oil into the smallest jar of the whole collection. She continued pouring … and filled it to the brim. Elijah carried it carefully across the room and placed it on a shelf. By the time he had picked his way back across the jar-strewn floor, she had filled a second, and a third, and a fourth.

Elijah and Aaron could not keep up with the speed that Mum was filling the jars. They ran out of shelf space, and still she kept on pouring. Elijah grabbed the biggest jar of the lot, and said, "Try this one." The oil gushed out of mum's jar, quickly filling the heavy pot.

Late into the night, by the light of the moon, the flood of oil continued. They laughed, and sang, and counted the jars.

Elijah saved a beautiful bronze jar until last. As the level of the oil climbed up its polished side, the flow began to falter. The top of the bronze jar was narrow and when the oil reached its slender neck, the flow slowed to a dribble. The last drop filled the jar to its shining rim.

Early the next morning, the three of them ran to tell Elisha. He was not surprised by their news.

"Sell it at the market" he told them, "and repay the moneylender. You can live off what is left."

An invisible army

2 Kings 6

Working for Elisha, the man of God, was often exciting, and usually exhausting, but Gehazi had never expected it to be dangerous.

He and Elisha were always on the move, travelling from village to village, telling people about God. When the war against Syria started, Gehazi was given a new and very important job, carrying messages from his master to the king. God would speak to Elisha, telling him where and how the Syrian army was planning to attack. Then Gehazi would run, as fast as he could, to tell the king in Samaria. When he arrived in the royal city – hot, filthy and utterly exhausted – the guards always ushered him straight in to see the king. How many other people his age did that? When he had delivered his message, Gehazi was treated like a prince. He washed in the palace, and was given rich food and fine clothes. While he enjoyed these luxuries, the Israelite army would be

alerted to the Syrian plans and lives would be saved. Wherever Gehazi went, he was always welcome; he was the hero of the moment.

The king of Syria was furious that the Israelites always knew his plans. He hunted for the spy among his staff. But his advisers told him, "There is no spy. There is a man of God in

Israel who tells his king everything you plan. He even tells his king what you say in your own bedroom."

"Find this man," the king of Syria commanded. "He must be stopped."

■ ■ ■

The day started normally. Elisha was visiting a small town called Dothan. Gehazi woke up as soon as it was light, dressed, and

set off towards the well, carrying an empty water jar. He soon sensed that something was wrong. There were none of the usual cheery greetings as he walked through the town. People were scowling at him.

Through an open window he heard a woman scream, "They'll kill us all!"

He slowed down, straining to pick up scraps

of conversation as he passed. "We'll have to hand them over," someone decided.

Gehazi continued his walk towards the town gate more cautiously. *Probably a Syrian raiding gang, spotted in the hills,* he thought.

The truth was far worse.

When Gehazi stepped through Dothan's modest wooden gateway, he saw a forest of spears and javelins. The entire Syrian army had surrounded the town. There were rows of chariots and war horses each carrying armed and armoured soldiers.

Gehazi froze. His face and fingers went numb. There was no hope of escape. He dropped his heavy water jar, but he never heard it smash; he just ran. It wasn't like running to Samaria with a message – that was gruelling work. His legs ran on their own, through the streets, across the market square, and up, up the steep hill. He had never run faster. At the top, he crashed, panting, into the house.

Elisha was as calm as ever. He barely seemed to notice that Gehazi was panting and coughing, white with fear.

"It's the Syrians!" Gehazi spluttered. "We're surrounded. What are we going to do?"

Elisha looked at his assistant steadily. Gehazi thought that his master hadn't understood. He tried again.

"The whole army is here," he explained breathlessly, "thousands of them."

Elisha was still untroubled. He gazed out of the window at the surrounding hills. "Those who are with us are far more than those who are with them," he stated quietly.

Gehazi was bewildered. He looked out of the same window. There was nothing but grass and rocks, and the occasional tree. He looked at Elisha. He was praying. Gehazi settled himself down against the wall. He knew not to interrupt when his master was talking with God.

"O Lord!" Elisha prayed. "Open his eyes and let him see."

Gehazi knew that the prayer was about him, but it didn't make any sense. His eyes worked perfectly well. Suddenly feeling fidgety, he stood up and walked round the room. He wanted to go outside, but it wouldn't be safe. For the first time in his life he wondered what it would be like to die.

He began to understand what the townspeople had been talking about earlier, and why none of them would look at him. They had decided to hand Elisha over. A thousand panics rushed through Gehazi's mind. His heart raced. He felt cold but was covered in sweat. He needed fresh air.

Gehazi slipped outside, despite the danger. He glanced up at the surrounding hills, and could not believe what he saw. All around

Dothan, the hills were crowded with horses and chariots, every one made of fire. There were tens of thousands of them, all blazing like the sun. And they were there – he had no doubt – to protect Elisha.

Gehazi had never seen an angel. He had heard of them, of course. Now he was looking at so many of the heavenly creatures that he could not tell where one ended and the next began. He ran back into the house. Elisha was smiling.

"We must go to the town gate," he said.

Gehazi said nothing. He handed the man of God his sandals and walking staff, and they strode swiftly down the deserted streets together.

When Elisha appeared in the gateway, the commander of the Syrian army rolled his chariot slowly forwards.

"My God," Elisha prayed steadily, "Make these people blind."

The armoured chariot stopped beside Elisha.

"Who are you looking for?" he asked the Syrian.

"Elisha, the prophet," the commander barked.

Elisha smiled. "You've come to the wrong place," he replied helpfully. "Follow me, and I'll take you to him." He set off purposefully down the road towards Samaria. The commander followed, and behind him came the whole Syrian army.

Gehazi jogged along beside his master, struggling to take it all in. He kept glancing from side to side, expecting to see the angels on their fiery horses – he knew they were there – but all he could see was the long line of Syrian soldiers marching ignorantly into the clutches of their enemy.

Elisha instructed Gehazi to run ahead and warn the king of Israel. So for the second time that day, his legs carried him effortlessly along, not – this time – from fear, but from sheer elation.

He had a message to deliver: "Open up the gates. God has given the Syrian army into your hands."

"Shall I kill them?" the king asked, rushing out to meet Gehazi.

"No," he replied. "Elisha says: Give them food and drink. Lay on a party. Then send them back to their king."

The Syrian army never troubled the towns of Israel again.

The smiling rabbi

Mark 5, Luke 8

Hannah woke up from a restless sleep. Her head was still screaming with pain, even worse than before.

Everyone was fussing. Hannah lay on her bed, and everyone else bustled around: her mother, her nan, her granny, and numerous aunts. There was always someone by her bed, cooing and stroking her arm, and saying, "Such a shame." The rest spent their time in a huddle at the other end of the room, talking in hushed voices so Hannah couldn't hear. But she knew what was happening. Even though no one had actually told her, Hannah knew she was dying.

People kept telling her that she would be all right, but she could tell that they didn't mean it. She was tired, utterly tired. Tired of the lies, tired of the constant pain, tired of the fuss and bother, tired of living.

It seemed to her, as she lay there, that she was the calmest one in the whole house. She wanted to stand up on her wretched bed and announce to the lot of them, "Don't make such a fuss. Millions of people have died before. It's

not that difficult." But she couldn't. All she could do was lie there. It was her mother's turn to crouch down with tear-filled eyes and hold her cold hand. Hannah squeezed her mum's fingers and tried to force a reassuring smile. She watched a lonely tear crawl down her mum's anxious face.

There was more whispering in the corner. Hannah caught a phrase. "He'll be here soon, I'm sure."

Someone else responded, but again she couldn't hear. Then the first voice replied, "He never says no."

Hannah didn't know who *he* was. Whoever he was, clearly everyone was waiting for him.

Her body seemed so heavy. Her head felt as if a hot knife was cutting it in half. Her feet were as cold as stone. A month ago, she had thought of death as an angry monster that would snatch away her soul when she least

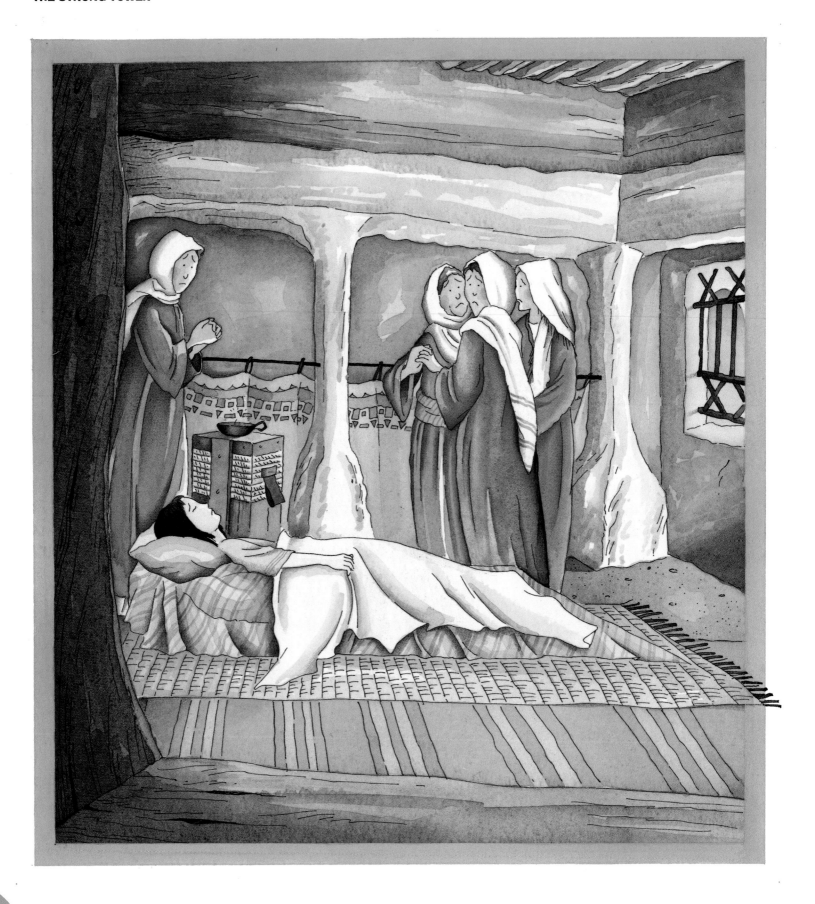

expected it. Now it seemed more like a gentle nurse who would carry her far from all this wretchedness. Her mum left her, and joined the rising argument in the corner of the room.

Peace. Hannah closed her eyes and let out a long low sigh. The voices faded. She experienced a rare moment of relief. She felt as though she was floating, surrounded by warmth, and she couldn't feel any pain. In fact, she felt absolutely fine – free. She savoured the moment.

There was a scream. It was her mum. Then everyone was screaming. They were awful, agonised screams, but somehow Hannah felt untroubled by them.

She looked calmly around the room. But it seemed to have disappeared. Only the people were still there, and she was looking down on them from where the ceiling should have been. All those screaming women were pressing around something. Or was it someone? Hannah looked closely from her vantage point above the chaos. It looked like a girl, a girl of about Hannah's age. Then it all made sense, wonderful sense. The girl was her, or rather her body. She had died.

She wanted to talk to them. She wanted to say, "I'm right here." But somehow she knew they wouldn't hear. Hannah turned away from her wailing relatives and wondered what would

happen next. She felt that she should wait. She didn't know what she was waiting for but it seemed the right thing to do. So she waited, and wondered why. Perhaps she was waiting for the man that her aunts had been waiting for a short while ago. She didn't know.

Suddenly Hannah became aware of the door, and it opened. Her dad walked in. He looked terrible. After him came three other men, and then ... light. It seemed that the doorway had simply filled with light, and the light was beautiful. A man walked in. He was an ordinary man but he seemed wonderfully bright. She recognised him. It was the Smiling Rabbi. That's what the children had called him. He had visited her father's synagogue before she was ill. He had told funny stories that made the children laugh, but her father was cross; the synagogue, he insisted, was not a place for silly jokes.

The Smiling Rabbi wasn't smiling now. He was talking to Hannah's relatives, telling them off.

"She's not dead," he told them firmly.

Her aunts laughed scornfully. "I think you'll find she is," one of them mocked.

Hannah was furious. "How dare you?" she shouted. "I'm right here." But none of them could hear her.

The Rabbi – what was his name? – Jesus,

made them all leave the house, everyone except her mum and dad, and his three friends. It was quiet.

Jesus crouched down and looked at Hannah's lifeless body. He was sad, but it was a warm sadness. She was drawn towards him. This is what she had been waiting for. She knew it now. She came closer. Jesus reached down and held her limp hand.

Hannah felt it! She felt his strong grip on her skin.

He spoke. "Little girl," he said, "Get up."

She opened her eyes. She was lying on her bed again. The room had returned. She was looking up at the ceiling and looking up at Jesus. He was smiling. It was the loveliest smile she had ever seen. She sat up and hugged him tightly. He laughed. Her mother screamed.

Her father looked astounded.

Hannah jumped up from the bed and into her dad's arms. Tears were pouring down his cheeks. His arms engulfed her and the two of them began to jump up and down together. Jesus was still laughing. His laugh seemed to be the music to which Hannah's excited jumping was the only dance. She bounced over to her mum, and they stood, holding each other's hands, beaming into one another's smiling faces. There were no words big enough or beautiful enough for that moment.

Jesus broke the silence. He placed a large, workman's hand on each of their shoulders and announced, "I think she needs something to eat."

A deadly secret

Acts 23

Jonathan was very scared.
He didn't know what to say,
and he didn't know what not to say.

The tall Roman centurion was staring at him. Jonathan smiled weakly at the man and then looked down at the engravings on the soldier's polished armour. He had never been this close to a Roman before. Sometimes he and his friends dared each other to run up behind a Roman soldier in the street and tap the back plate of his armour. Once or twice, his friends had been rewarded with a sharp jab from the blunt end of the soldier's spear. But standing right next to one in a dark corridor was quite another matter. Jonathan kept a close eye on the man's short, flat sword, and wondered how many people it had killed.

Whenever Jonathan went out into the city on his own, his mum always told him:

"Keep away from the Romans, and keep out of trouble."

Since his Uncle Paul had been arrested by the Romans, she was even more concerned.

Now he was right in the middle of trouble – serious trouble. He was standing outside the door of the top Roman commander in all Jerusalem.

You haven't done anything wrong, Jonathan reminded himself. But even though that was true, he still felt guilty.

"Just say what you overheard," had been his Uncle Paul's advice. But Jonathan was not convinced. It would be much safer to say nothing. He had only told his teacher in the first place because the plot concerned his own mum's brother. Then his teacher said he would have to tell Uncle Paul, and Uncle Paul had insisted that he tell the commander. So here he was, right beside a fully-armed soldier, in the barracks where Uncle Paul was a prisoner.

If that gang find out it was me who dobbed on them, he warned his already frightened self, they'll kill me too.

Jonathan looked up at the centurion. It was too late to run away. He was almost as safely locked inside the barracks as his uncle. (Paul was chained to a stone pillar in the guard room.)

The commander's door opened silently. A dark-haired gentleman in a white toga invited him in. Was this the commander? He didn't know. He had never actually seen Commander Claudius, although he had heard plenty about him; everyone in Jerusalem hated the man.

"Sir," the centurion said, "the prisoner, Paul, asked me to bring this young man to you. He has something to tell you."

The dark-haired man was the commander.

The centurion shut the door and stood in front of it, hand on sword. Now Jonathan had no chance of escape, and no one to help him. He was frightened of the Romans; he was terrified of the gang that was planning to kill his uncle. He would have to decide by himself what to say, and what not to say.

Commander Claudius stepped into the middle of the room and studied him. Jonathan tried to look into his eyes, but couldn't. He looked at the floor. The commander spoke. His voice was friendly, not at all what Jonathan expected.

"What's your name, young man?"

"Jonathan," he mumbled, still looking at the floor.

"Why did you come to see Paul?"

Jonathan looked up at the man. "He's my uncle."

He quickly looked down to the floor again. Be careful, he warned himself, if you say too much you could land yourself in even more trouble.

Commander Claudius reached out a strong arm and took Jonathan's hand. He led him to the window, and crouched down so that their eyes were at the same level.

"Now," he said softly, so the centurion couldn't hear, "what is it you want to tell me?"

Want to tell you? He thought with a rush of panic. I don't want to tell you anything.

His mum's voice echoed up into his mind: Keep away from the Romans, Jon. It was way too late for that!

He wondered what his friends would say if they could see him now. They would say: …Never trust a Roman. That was what everyone in Jerusalem said.

But the grey eyes of Commander Claudius said the opposite. They said: It's all right, you can trust me.

The commander let go of Jonathan's hand and gazed out of the window. Jonathan relaxed, just a little. The window looked across to the huge stone wall of the Temple. It was there that Uncle Paul had been arrested. It was there that

Jonathan had overheard some of the Jewish extremists plotting to kill him. And it was in that very street, between the barracks and the Temple, that they were waiting to ambush him and kill him, because they hated Paul for his belief in Jesus.

Jonathan knew he had to say something. Paul's life depended on it.

Ten minutes ago, Uncle Paul had looked at Jonathan with his dark, piercing eyes and said, "Just tell the commander what you heard." It had seemed such simple advice when he said it. But now that Jonathan was on his own, he didn't know what to do.

Commander Claudius turned round and looked at him.

"What do you *want* to tell me?" He emphasised the *want*, and it unlocked Jonathan's indecision.

He decided to say everything. He was just about to start, when all the muddled fears of his upbringing surged into his mind, shouting: You can't trust the Romans!

He was stuck again.

A favourite phrase of Uncle Paul's floated into his thoughts. Whatever happens, thank God. Not knowing what else to do, Jonathan felt that he should give it a try.

"Almighty God," he prayed above the confusion in his thoughts, "thank you. Thank

you … that this Roman … is a kind man. I didn't think he would be. Amen."

Almost immediately, the storm in Jonathan's head was calmed. It was quite clear to him what he should do.

"The religious leaders are going to ask you to take my Uncle Paul back to their Council," he told the commander. "They will say that they need to ask him more questions."

The man nodded, inviting him to continue.

"Don't do it," Jonathan said, with more confidence than he thought possible. "A gang of forty men is going to ambush him. They have vowed not to eat or drink anything until Uncle Paul is dead." He paused. Had he said

everything? Not quite. "It's all arranged," he added. "The only thing they need is for you to take him down the road."

The commander stood upright. "Thank you," he said politely. "I will have Paul taken to a safe place tonight."

Then he looked out of his window at the street below. A smile crept across his face. Jonathan had never seen a Roman smile. It quite surprised him.

"Somewhere down there," Claudius said with a slightly mischievous chuckle, "there are going to be forty very hungry and very thirsty men."

Guidance notes

Abandoned in the desert

Possible issues: sibling rivalry, blended families, broken home, anger.

When we look at Ishmael's story we can see many reasons for his anger. He feels pushed out by his new baby brother and rejected by his dad. He has a difficult relationship with his dad's new wife too. These situations are very common today, and children may well relate to them and feel that Ishmael was badly treated and was justified to behave as he did.

Family relationships can be very complex now and none of us is perfect. Favouritism is very dangerous, but can creep in. However, it is worth being clear with children that there is a difference between having strong feelings and acting on them in an inappropriate way.

The following questions may be useful to start discussion:

- Think of a time when you lost your temper. What happened?
- Is there something you could have done differently. What is it? It may be helpful to make suggestions here; go out of the room, count to ten, send up an arrow prayer or think of a favourite song/TV programme. You could even share what you do.
- Talk about some of the good, and some of the not so good, things about having brothers/sisters.
- Sometimes we don't get on with someone in our family, or we feel we are treated differently to others. Can you tell me if anything like that has happened to you?

Some issues to explore:

- Anger management;
- Expressing feelings in a safe and appropriate way;
- Living in a family, the ups and downs;
- God keeps his promises.

Jealous brothers

Possible issues: stepfamily conflict, bullying/favouritism, being special, fear.

So much for being special and a favourite. Joseph ended up in fear for his life and then sold as a slave! When we read this story we need to be aware of the unpalatable thought that our children might be the bully or the bullied, so it is worth exploring to which character in the story they relate. It is also worth noting that Joseph had a different mum to his brothers, and she was a favourite too. Children reading this story may be very well aware of the feelings that are stirred up when families split and blend.

The following questions may be useful to start discussion:

- Is there a part of the story which makes you think of your family?
- What do you think it is like to be bullied by others older or bigger than you? What would you do?
- Do you know someone who is a favourite? How do you feel about them? (Talk about any behaviour you may be aware of.)
- Do you think you've ever been somebody's favourite? What do you think X (the non-favourite in the situation) felt about that?
- Joseph had a really scary experience, trapped in a dry well. Can you tell me about a scary experience you've had?

Some things to remember:

- Make sure children know what to do if they are being bullied.
- Listen carefully and take their fears seriously while offering reassurance.
- Families are not always the safe havens we would like them to be. Think about how each family member is treated by you and others, and be aware of the dangers of favouritism. Family life is not about treating everyone the same; children all have their own unique needs. However, they have a strong sense of justice so it is important to treat them fairly and make sure they all experience the unconditional love they need.

The brave sister

Possible issues: caring for a brother or sister, being brave, answers to prayer, taking risks.

Children may be called upon to be carers. It may just be a bit of babysitting; others take on responsibility for their siblings from quite a young age and for considerable lengths of time. Sometimes when children play out together, a dangerous situation may arise where older siblings act to protect their younger brothers or sisters. Children may have mixed feelings about such responsibilities, they may resent such expectations or they may feel proud that their parents trust them. This could be explored after the story; why was it Miriam and not her mum who had to make sure Moses was OK? Do you think she wanted to do it?

The following questions may be useful to start discussion:

- What is the most "brave, crazy, clever, or wonderful thing" you've ever done?
- Tell me about a time you helped, or were helped by a brother or sister.
- Miriam holds her breath and her heart beats very fast. She was afraid. Tell me about a time you felt like that.
- Did someone help you? If so, who and how?

If a child is unable to think of something brave that they have done, do prompt them and ensure they come up with something you can reinforce positively. Never miss an opportunity to build self-esteem by offering praise and encouragement. If a child shares a frightening experience do not try to play it

down. Things which seem harmless to us may be very real to them. Listen carefully and offer reassurance. Make sure they know how to stay safe; there is some good literature available on this subject.

Miriam was not really alone in this story. She prays to God, as she has been taught to do by her mum. Sometimes we forget that children need to be shown how to pray. Most effective of all is to lead by example; let children see that we pray in difficult circumstances, and share with them when God answers. When Miriam approaches the princess, her fear disappears and she is filled with calm. God did not answer the prayer in the way Miriam expected; in fact he did the opposite by letting the princess discover Moses! However, the end result was Moses' rescue.

Some issues to explore:

- Caring for siblings: tiresome or something to be proud of?
- Being afraid: who is there to help?
- Prayer: make sure children know how to pray and to expect answers.

See also: *A voice in the night*

A night of panic

Possible issues: dealing with family, bullying, teasing, fear and change, being different (because of a parent).

For children, parents can be a mixed blessing! This is well illustrated in this story. My dad, the hero. My dad, the idiot. What must it be like to have a famous dad? It certainly draws attention to you; there you are at the head of the crowd, proudly holding dad's hand; but then

remember when no one wanted to be your friend, because of your dad?

Perhaps your parent is a church leader? Everyone knows you as "the vicar's kids". There is a pressure to be seen to be good, and friends at school think your dad is weird. Or perhaps dad is not really famous, just not like other people's dads. Perhaps he looks different, speaks differently, perhaps you do not live with him. He could be an asylum seeker, a headmaster, in the army, in prison.

These are some issues to explore: Remember to listen first, then reassure or just acknowledge that yes, sometimes it is hard to be pushed into the spotlight. It may lead to bullying which so often is based on something we cannot change; our colour, size or who is in our family.

Gershom was blessed to have a father who was obedient to God and served him. However, that meant being constantly on the move. Children will experience change throughout life; moving house, changing schools, different people coming in and out of their lives. These unsettling experiences may be an opportunity to talk about God as our Heavenly Father, always there, ready to listen and loving us unconditionally (see Matthew 7:9–11).

The following questions may be useful to start discussion:

- Who would you choose to be in this story and why?
- How do you think Gershom felt about his dad?
- Gershom had to move more than once. What do you think it was like? What would you miss if you had to move? (Rephrase if you know they have moved.)

- How would you feel if your parents were less well known?
- What is it like when a good friend drops you?

Some issues to explore:
- Parents, as heroes or as a cause of bullying. Our Heavenly Father.
- Change: the excitement and the feelings of loss.
- Fear: who is there for the child in scary situations?
- Being different yourself. Peer pressure and the need to conform (as opposed to bullying).

A voice in the night

Possible issues: what a family is, change, moving, family relationships, coping with responsibility.

What is a family? There is no simple answer. Children may live with a single parent, a grandparent, foster-carers, two parents or one parent and their new partner. There may be stepbrothers or sisters, or different children coming and going. Samuel no longer lives with his mum and he misses her, as he only sees her once a year. Mum's gift of a cloak is a reminder of her.

Children can be very frightened by the lifestyle of older members of a family: for example, partying, if it involves drinking, makes for volatile, aggressive or unpredictable adults. This situation makes children feel very unsafe. How effective would Eli be in protecting Samuel from harm? This aspect of the story may trigger memories, and a child may need to talk them through with you.

Sometimes children can be anxious about telling the truth if they think that we won't like what they have to say, and this can be a real burden for them. Once again, we can only attempt to keep the lines of communication open, listen and try not to jump in quickly with our own explanations or justifications.

The following questions may be useful to start discussion:
- Is there a part of the story which makes you think of your family? In what way?
- What do you keep to remind you of your family members?
- Why do you think Samuel is frightened of Eli's sons?
- What difficult jobs have you had to do?

Some issues to explore:
- Feelings around separation from family members;
- Fear of older brothers/sisters;
- Being chosen for an important task and carrying it through.

You're only a child

Possible issues: feeling small/ unimportant, bullying, trusting God.

David was small and unimportant; children often feel like this. However, David had a strong sense of self-esteem and confidence, knew his own strengths and abilities and called on God's help. These are things we need to develop in children through praise, encouragement and example.

David's confidence comes out of his faith; he says to Goliath "I come against you in the name of God." Once again we can use these stories to illustrate that we

have a God who we can rely on and trust to be with us in all situations.

The following questions may be useful to start discussion:
- Is there a part of the story which makes you think of your family?
- What do you think it is like to be bullied by others older or bigger than you? What would you do?
- When was the last time you were brave? (Help the child here if they struggle. Were they scared going to school for the first time? When they were in a certain situation? Show how being scared is the first step to being brave!)
- Why do you think David decided to fight Goliath?

Some issues to explore:
- Feelings of unimportance or irrelevance due to being a child;
- Gaining confidence;
- Trusting God.

See also: *Jealous brothers*

The miraculous oil jar

Possible issues: being unpopular, loss of a parent, trusting God, fear of the unknown/change, life is not fair!

This story reflects what can be the grim reality of bereavement and its effect on a family; loneliness, financial hardship, isolation, loss of status and of faith in God.

The following questions may be useful to start discussion:

- What was life like for Elijah Junior before his dad died? What was life like afterwards?
- Elijah Junior said, "It's not fair." Have you ever felt like that? Tell me about it.
- No one wanted to know Elijah and his family, what do you think that was like? Have you ever felt like that? When?
- When was the last time you felt really angry? (Anger is a way that grief may express itself.)

We need to be careful that in keeping things simple for children, we are not simplistic and don't leave them thinking that prayer is a magic wand to get us out of trouble. Even as adults we can struggle with the notion of unanswered prayer if we fail to have an understanding of the way in which Jesus taught us to pray.

Some things to remember:

- Children may suffer as a result of the role of others in their family, eg dad as church leader.
- Don't make assumptions about reactions to bereavement, listen.
- There are some excellent resources available about bereavement; I refer you to the bibliography at the end of the book.

- Sometimes life is unfair but God is with us in all situations.
- If the child is grieving in some way, it is likely they are not the only person in the family to be affected. It is worth drawing out from the child how a parent/sibling may be feeling/acting at this time and how this affects them.

See also: *A night of panic.* You might like to look at the comments about that story, famous dads and the effects on their children.

An invisible army

Possible issues: fear, using our gifts, reassurance, listening to God, trusting God when everything seems hopeless.

Children often value some skills/talents above others, and tend to disregard or devalue their own gifts. Sadly, sometimes children's experiences in school, or even within their families, reinforce this and affect their self-esteem. Helping children recognise their gifts and use them is an important task for any parent/carer.

It would be helpful to look again at the comments/questions relating to Miriam's and Samuel's story, both were given important and dangerous tasks to do and experienced fear as a result. They also learned to trust God. What this story helps to draw out is that even though we can't see God, he is there with us in the difficult times. It was only after Elisha prayed, that Gehazi was able to see the hosts of angels protecting them, but they were already there.

The following questions may be useful to start discussion:

- What difficult jobs have you had to do?
- When did you last feel really scared? Did someone help you? How did you stop feeling scared, or are you still a bit scared?
- What are you really good at? (If the child struggles with this, make sure you've got something to say to help them out.)

Some issues to explore:

- Being chosen for an important task and carrying it through;
- Trusting God/knowing God is there;
- Perspective is everything! Gehazi was terrified until he saw things as they really were. Is there a way to calm a child's fears by presenting them with reality?

See also: *The brave sister* and *A voice in the night.*

The smiling rabbi

Possible issues: death, dying, bereavement, fear.

In general, death is not dealt with very well in our society. It is something to be talked about in hushed whispers, something children should be protected from. However, as Christians, we are clear that death is not the end, and we are not without hope. That is not to say that we do not grieve: John tells us that Jesus wept at the death of Lazarus (John 11:35).

For children who are facing death, we need to be honest and brave enough to hear their fears, yet ready to give reassurance. Hannah describes her own impending death in two ways; an angry monster and later, a gentle nurse. In the end she came to accept, even welcome death as a peaceful release. However, we can be reassured that life after death is real. Jesus demonstrates his power over death by bring Hannah back to life.

The way in which children are affected by bereavement can be similar to how they react to other stresses in life; after all, it's about dealing with loss and change. Each child will respond differently, but a loss of confidence is to be expected, along with sadness, depression, anger, bitterness and regrets.

As a result of the way we sometimes shield children from death, they can develop strange or irrational ideas or fears about it. The only way we will know what children understand about death is to talk about it.

The following questions may be useful to start discussion:

- What happens to Hannah in the story?
- What do you think happens when you die?
- Was Hannah afraid to die? If not, why?
- Hannah describes death as an angry monster, but also as a gentle nurse. What do you think of when you think of dying?
- What did Jesus do?

This is certainly not a subject for a one-off conversation. Children are going to encounter death and dying in their reading, and particularly on the TV. The news, soaps and children's programmes will offer opportunities to bring up the subject in a natural way. As always, we do not have all the answers but we do know that Jesus overcame death once and for all.

Some issues to explore:

- Jesus has conquered death, death is not the end.
- Fear is a natural response to what we do not understand. Preparing children and being honest about death and dying are all important.
- Strong and confused feelings are natural following bereavement, no matter how much faith we have.
- As always, listen first and don't assume any particular response.

A deadly secret

Possible issues: fear, confusion, prejudice, secrets, telling tales.

Sometimes the messages we give children are unhelpful and contradictory. Don't be a telltale. Why didn't you tell me you were being bullied? If you are in trouble, ask a police officer, or the lady in the shop for help. Don't talk to strangers. Teaching whom to trust is an important lesson of childhood, and sometimes our prejudices will damage children's ability to trust.

The following questions may be useful to start discussion:

- Have you ever had a big secret you were afraid to tell?
- Did you tell and what happened?
- Who can you trust?

Some things to remember:

- Children need to know that telling is OK.
- They can share their fears, worries and concerns with us and we will respond appropriately.
- Listen carefully, and take what is said seriously.
- Reassure and take action if necessary.
- Be aware of your prejudices.

Sue Phipps

Useful information

General Parenting

■ **Christian Family Network** Their vision is to provide a place where you can receive the support, advice and encouragement you need to help your family live and grow God's way. You can subscribe to receive news, advice, resources and reviews etc.

> Christian Family Network (CMC)
> Garcia Estate
> Canterbury Rd
> Worthing
> West Sussex
> BN13 1EH
> www.cfnetwork.co.uk

■ **Care for the Family** produce lots of good resources on parenting. Their series of books called *Parentalk* includes a guide to brothers and sisters, sibling rivalry etc.

> Care for the Family
> PO Box 488
> Cardiff
> CF15 7YY
> www.careforthefamily.org.uk

■ **www.parentscentre.gov.uk** A useful site primarily about children's education and learning, but which also includes pages on bullying. Also provides extensive lists of links to other sites to help and inform parents on relevant issues.

■ **NSPCC** On the website there are advice pages and downloadable leaflets for young people and parents, that cover bullying and safety issues. You can also write and request a

'Parenting pack' that includes sample leaflets, sending an A4 envelope and five 1st class stamps to:

> NSPCC Publications
> Weston House
> 42 Curtain Road
> London
> EC2A 3NH
> www.nspcc.org.uk

Divorce and family breakdown

■ **NCH** The Children's charity has a website specifically for children about this issue; www.itsnotyourfault.org There is also a general website www.nch.org.uk that has advice about children using the Internet safely, and self-harm.

Bullying

■ **Kidscape** are a national charity that work to help prevent bullying and child abuse. Online advice, support and downloadable leaflets are available from the website and the FAQ are very good. There is also a list of publications.

> Kidscape
> 2 Grosvenor Gardens
> London
> SW1W 0DH
> www.kidscape.org.uk

■ **Bullying Online** Another good website that also includes a wonderful list of links to useful sites on anything

from bullying and drugs, through to becoming a school governor. www.bullying.co.uk

Bereavement

■ **The Youth Involvement Project** have developed a website by children, for children; www.rd4u.org.uk. Take a look at this yourself first. It is very good but doesn't pull any punches.

■ **Winston's Wish** As well as a website, there is a very good booklist available here that includes books for children and parents/carers.

> Winston's Wish
> Clara Burgess Centre
> Bayshill Road
> Cheltenham
> GL50 3AW
> www.winstonswish.org.uk

■ **Channel4 Health House** have an excellent website with pages on children's bereavement, information on how to support children, and a comprehensive list of resources and books. www.channel4.com/health

■ **BBC** also has some good pages on their website on how we can help children. www.bbc.co.uk/health/bereavement

■ **Childhood Bereavement Trust** This organisation provides a lot of support to agencies, but also has a good website with pages for young people. This includes recommended

reading, but it is perhaps better suited to older children. However, the site provides useful links to other sites, and in particular includes local organisations that provide counselling.

> Childhood Bereavement Trust
> Ashton House
> High Street
> West Wycombe
> High Wycombe
> HP14 3AG
> www.childbereavement.org.uk/
> youngpeople

■ **Childline** has a national phone helpline for children to discuss their worries about anything; 0800 1111 also www.childline.org.uk

■ **Kids Helpline** (Australia) is a freephone counselling service for children aged 5 to 18 who need to talk with someone (phone 1800 55 1800). A 24 hour service for children in Australia. Web counselling is also available free at www.kidshelpline.com.au